The Leprosy Bell

Margaret Williams MBE

A catalogue record for this book is available from the British Library

ISBN 978-1-5272-9514-8

Printed by CPI Group (UK) Croydon CR0 4YY

Acknowledgements

*Cover design by Elizabeth Dixon of
Abstract Communications Ltd.*

Photos by Janet French

Proof reading by Diana Swann

Typesetting by Geoff Fisher

"Promoting Christ Church to the Community"

Any profits generated from the sale of these books will be divided between "The Friends of Christ Church" and "The Leprosy Mission "

The Friends of Christ Church Swindon is a registered charity to raise funds for the maintenance and enhancement of this Grade 2 listed building. Christ Church is the parish church of Swindon, Old Town and is where the author of this book worships.

The Leprosy Mission is a Christian charity that works to find and cure leprosy in the world today. The Leprosy Mission works with people of all faiths and none to defeat this disabling disease and transform the lives of those affected.

Isaac is a well respected and successful citizen of Capernaum, on the Sea of Galilee, when he is struck down with the dreaded disease of leprosy. This changed his life in more ways than one. Although Isaac is a fictional character, his life story draws upon facts recorded in the gospels.

Prologue

"Grandad, why do you keep that little bell and that pebble on that shelf?" said Joseph to his grandfather. Isaac looked at his enquiring grandson with a long, hard look and said, "One day, you will know why these are so important to me. I will tell you the whole story when you are older but in the meantime, just promise me that you will never throw away these two things as they represent such a big part in your grandfather's life and, in a way, your life too and one day you will understand this."

With that, Isaac took his grandson's hand and they walked from his house down the hill to the seashore for their usual evening walk. The sea was calm and the sun was low in the sky making the water on the Sea of Galilee shimmer in the dying evening sun. Along the shore they walked towards the fishing boats which were anchored and where some of the fishermen were preparing to go out fishing, their nets having been laid out to dry in the warm sunshine during the day were now being carefully placed in the boats. The sea was so calm that Isaac remarked that he thought it would be a good night for fishing whereupon Joseph asked, "Why do they go out fishing at night? I think it would be better to go out in the daytime when they could see where the fish were." "Well," said Isaac, "you had better ask the fishermen that. Look some of the men who work for Simon Peter and Andrew are over there, go and ask them." So, leaving his grandfather, Joseph ran over to talk to the fishermen leaving Isaac staring out over the calm waters of the Sea of Galilee. Isaac watched his grandson and remembered how he had asked similar questions when he was his age, watching the same or similar boats going out in the evening and then returning in the early dawn sunshine with their catch of fish. It was a hard life for when they landed their catch, there was still work to do; the fish had to be sorted and the nets hung out to dry in the sun before they could sell the fish to the local people. Isaac remembered how he would sometimes go down to the fishermen in the early morning, before they had breakfast as the earlier you went the better the choice of fish there would be and then there would be the banter between his mother and the fishermen as to the price to pay with his mother saying that the asking price was too much and eventually a price was agreed upon and all was well.

Yes, life in Capernaum had not changed much since those early days and yet, and yet, Isaac's life had changed dramatically, such changes that he would never have dreamed of or thought possible. Yes, one day he would tell his story to Joseph, his grandson and not only to Joseph but to others, too as it was important, important not just to his grandson and to his family but important for generations to come --- they should know!

Chapter 1

One of Isaac's earliest memories was playing in his father's workshop with the wood shavings and the sawdust, he used to cover a piece of wood with sawdust and then draw pictures in the sawdust with his finger as one would in the sand down at the seashore. His father was a carpenter and there was enough work to keep him busy as Capernaum was a busy town and there were always people wanting things made from wood. Isaac would watch his father change a rough piece of wood into a table or a stool, first sawing the wood and getting it into the right shape and size and then making it smooth and beautiful. The wood shavings which fell to the floor as he worked were great to play with and Isaac remembered how he would find long curly bits and join them together and make unusual shapes out of them. He would spend hours in the workshop with his dad and he would meet many of the local people who came to buy the things his father made or, sometimes, they would bring something that needed some repair and Isaac's father was always happy to oblige.

Sometimes one of the fishermen would come in and ask him if he would do a repair on one of their boats which meant a walk down the hill to the shore to see the boat that needed a piece of wood replacing and Isaac liked going down with his father to see what was needed. This didn't happen often because most of the fishermen were very resourceful people and would attempt most repairs on their boats themselves so when a request came to Isaac's father it was usually something that would require a fair bit of skill.

Isaac had an older sister, Rebekah, but she usually played with the other girls who lived nearby and she loved going to the well with her mother in the mornings and the evenings when many of the women who lived nearby would gather to get the water but they would also linger to chat and hear all the latest news and gossip. Sometimes Isaac would go along too and then Rebekah would be given the task of looking after him as the women shared their stories. Isaac often wondered what they found to talk about but, whatever it was, it seemed to keep them happy.

When Isaac was old enough he went to the synagogue school. The synagogue was not far from their house and was right on the seashore. Rebekah did not go to school, girls didn't but on the Sabbath day they all went to the synagogue together as a family. When they arrived Isaac's father would go into the main part of the synagogue and Isaac would go with Rebekah and his mum upstairs to the part where all the women and children went. Isaac's father used to tell him how much he was looking forward to the time after his 12th birthday when he would take him to the part where all the men went to worship and Isaac looked forward to that too.

When Isaac was at synagogue school he had to learn to read the scriptures which he did but he would much rather have been at his father's workshop making things or walking along the seashore and finding interesting pieces of driftwood or unusually shaped pebbles and he would return with them to the workshop and see if he could make something out of them. Rebekah would some-times smile at his efforts but Isaac thought she didn't have enough imagination to see that a particular piece of drift-wood he had found could be made into a little boat. Once he persuaded her to part with a handkerchief which he fixed onto a piece of driftwood as a sail and then per-suaded her to accompany him down to the seashore to try it out. He remembered his squeals of delight when it floated on the crest of the waves but his disappointment when Rebekah wanted her handkerchief back when they got home! The problem was solved when Isaac's mum gave him a piece of fabric from a garment she was making, so that saved the day!

Of course, they were living under Roman rule at this time and there was a military presence always around Capernaum because there was a Roman garrison on the outskirts of the town. Isaac was used to seeing Roman sol-diers around Capernaum but his father used to say, "Don't bother them and they won't bother you" but when his father got together with the other men of the town, you could feel their dislike of the Roman occupation of their country. Sometimes, a couple of the soldiers would come into Isaac's father's workshop asking for something to be made for the garrison. They would ask how much the item would be and they would always try to get it made for less than his father asked so his father got wise to this and would start by telling them a price above the actual cost in the hope that he would get the proper price after a bit of bargaining!

There was one time in the year which Isaac really looked forward to and that was Passover time as they would try to go to Jerusalem as a family. This was so excit-ing as they would camp on the way to the city and camp outside the city when they got there. Camping on the journey was such fun as the boys would all meet up and play games while the men would be erecting the tents to sleep in and the mothers would be busy preparing food for them all to eat. Isaac did remember one occasion when they were all travelling up to Jerusalem and they had all stopped for the night when the boys began playing with some others who were travelling along but Isaac's father called him and was really cross with him and said he was not to play with the group he had joined. When Isaac had asked, "Why?" his father said it was because the other boys were Samaritans and good Jews did not mix with Samaritans! Isaac wondered why this was so, but as he grew older he was told that Samaritans were not pure Jews like they were and, as such, they must not have anything to do with them! As Isaac grew much older and, perhaps a little wiser, he began to doubt the Jewish teaching on this.

The city was full of people and Isaac remembered thinking that all the people in the whole world must have come to Jerusalem as he had never seen such crowds and there were many more Roman soldiers mingling among the crowds; in fact there were so many soldiers that Isaac wondered if there were any Roman soldiers left in Rome, surely they must all be in Jerusalem! His father said that it was not always like this, they drafted in more soldiers at Passover time and at other Jewish festivals because they were afraid there might be trouble with such large numbers gathering in one city.

Isaac's mother impressed upon him that he must stay close to them when they were in the city as they didn't want him to get lost among the crowds. They would go to the Temple which was huge and had lots of courtyards.

They would climb up the many steps to the first court where people who were not Jewish would go and then he and Rebekah and their mother would go through to the next part where all the women and children worshipped and learned, while his father went on to the next court where all the men and older boys went; Isaac looked forward to the time when he would be old enough to go with his father into that part of the temple but that would be when he was 12 years old.

Outside the Temple and in the narrow streets of Jerusalem, there were the sounds and the smells of the city; Isaac had never experienced anything quite like it, the smells of food cooking by the street sellers and the aroma of the bunches of herbs being sold; the air was filled with the sounds of the city, the tinkling of bells worn around the necks of the sheep and goats, the braying of the donkeys being goaded on by their impatient owners and the occasional group of people chanting from the scriptures as they made their way through the narrow streets towards the Temple. Isaac was fascinated by all this, it was all so different from his home town of Capernaum but it was exciting!

Life in Capernaum was not as busy as in the city of Jerusalem and although Isaac enjoyed the excitement of the city, he did enjoy his home town. It was here that his family were, here his roots were, here he felt safe and he felt he belonged. Also he enjoyed the sea and that was something which Jerusalem did not have. Isaac loved the seashore. The sea fascinated him with the ever changing waves. Sometimes the waves would be no larger than silver ripples on the water but when a storm was coming, those tiny, glistening waves became knee high and white and frothy, crashing against the pebbles on the shore. As the wind blew, the boats would move up and down like see-saws and they would make creaking sounds and the ropes that tied the sails would clang against the tall masts. After a storm, the sea would regain its peaceful, shimmering appearance and the shore would be littered with new pebbles thrown up by the waves, pebbles of different colours, some more grey than others, some more pink. Isaac would collect some of these and wonder how old they were; had they been on the seabed for years and years and, if so, where had they come from in the first place?

Sometimes, one of the fishermen would offer to take Isaac and his friends for a trip on a boat and sometimes Isaac and the family would go by boat across the sea to Cana where they would enjoy a picnic and then return by boat. They were happy, carefree days.

How well Isaac remembered the Passover after his 12th birthday; this was a really special Passover because, for the first time, Isaac was able to go with his father into the Court for Hebrew men at the Temple. In Hebrew terms Isaac was considered to be a man and although he had been able to go into the men's part of the synagogue in Capernaum since his birthday, to go into the men's part of the Temple in Jerusalem was something really special. That was quite a year for Isaac, there was his birthday when family, friends and neighbours all came together to celebrate with a family meal and his father gave a speech saying how proud he was of his son. On the following Sabbath day he went proudly into the local synagogue with all the men. That was a week to remember.

After that week Isaac spent far more time in the workshop with his father, learning the trade of carpentry. Of course, he already possessed the basic skills of carpentry because of the many hours he had spent in his father's workshop but as Isaac's father was such a skilled carpenter who was held in high esteem by the local people, there was much to learn on Isaac's part, specially about the handling of customers which Isaac's father did with much skill, diplomacy and patience!

Then, later, when Isaac got older, life in Capernaum was quite exciting. Many of the local youths and girls would meet down on the seashore and sometimes one of the fishermen would offer to take them out in their boat. Isaac liked that, it was so peaceful on the Sea of Galilee on a calm day but he knew that the weather could change quite suddenly and dramatically and the wind would howl around the boats and it could sound quite frightening. Isaac was glad he wasn't a fisherman as he wouldn't have liked being caught out in a storm at sea but most of these fishermen were used to that. However, even they were a little cautious when they saw dark clouds gathering in the north.

But Isaac remembered how he found the company of the local girls quite exciting. They would gather around the well and Isaac and some of the other teenage boys would pretend that they were just passing by when, in actual fact their sole purpose was to go to the well to meet up with the girls! Isaac remembered one particular day when he was with the other lads when one of the girls brought her cousin with her to the well; she lived in another village and had come to visit. Isaac thought she was beautiful and they smiled at each other. He discovered her name was Rachel and Isaac was anxious to know when she would be visiting her cousin again and was disappointed to hear that her cousin didn't know.

Each day after that Isaac kept looking at the girls gathering together at the well in the hope that Rachel might come again but weeks passed with no sign of her and then, in early autumn when the olives were being harvested from the trees and the vines were stripped of their luscious grapes, Rachel came again to visit her cousin and Isaac felt his heart miss a beat as he saw her. This time she was with her mother as well as her cousin at the well. After that brief encounter, Isaac didn't see her. Time passed and Isaac's father decided that the time had come to find a wife for Isaac and so he came home from the meeting at the synagogue one day and said that he had been speaking to the tent-maker from the next village who had a daughter of similar age to Isaac and who could be considered as a future wife for him. Isaac listened but thought how he wished the girl could have been Rachel whom he had seen at the well with her cousin. He wondered what had become of Rachel since he last saw her, maybe she had been betrothed to someone by this time. A meeting was arranged by Isaac's father with the tent-maker's family and Isaac remembered how his heart nearly missed a beat when he discovered that the daughter was in fact Rachel! So, at the appropriate time they were betrothed and that was the beginning of a lifelong love affair!

In due course the marriage was arranged; it was a joyful occasion with the family celebrations lasting a few days as weddings did. Isaac's sister, Rebekah had already married and was living quite close by so she was able to help Isaac's mother. As the wedding day approached, Isaac was really excited and his friends came knocking at the door ready to accompany him from his house to Rachel's. Rachel was awaiting him with her bridesmaids and Isaac took her back to his house. The next day was the formal part of the ceremony and Isaac remembered it very well. Rachel looked so beautiful dressed in white with flowers in her hair and Isaac dressed in ceremonial clothes as bridegrooms did. All their friends, relatives and neighbours were gathered there and beneath a canopy he and Rachel made their wedding vows and then the rejoicing began. It was autumn so the days were cooler and the evenings were very pleasant so the celebrations continued well into that night and the following nights.

By this time, Isaac did much of the work in the workshop and they made enough money from the carpentry business to keep them going and eighteen months after their wedding a baby girl was born to them and they called her Sarah and just over two years later a baby boy was born and they called him John.

Chapter 2

Isaac was a good carpenter but what he liked doing most of all was carving figures out of pieces of wood. He would spend hours working on a piece of olive wood making it into an animal or a small figurehead; this was something he enjoyed doing more than the everyday carpentry which they did, in fact, his reputation of carving began to take off and people would be happy to buy his unique pieces. It was not unusual for one of the Roman soldiers to come and buy one of his carvings to take back home to Italy when they went back to their homeland after doing their period of duty.

Life in Capernaum had not changed much, that is, the everyday life, but then came a man called Jesus, he came to the town and befriended Simon and Andrew, the fishermen brothers and, looking back Isaac could see how he had changed everything for some of them; Simon and Andrew were mesmerised by what Jesus said; in fact Jesus even changed Simon's name, calling him Peter, the rock!

When Isaac first heard about Jesus he was quite worried as he heard he was a carpenter from Nazareth and Isaac wondered if he intended setting up a business in Capernaum; would that be in opposition to Isaac's business? Was there a need for another carpenter in Capernaum? Would there be sufficient business to warrant another carpenter in the town? But all these fears were set aside as he spoke with Simon and Andrew and discovered that Jesus had left his carpentry and was now an itinerant preacher and teacher. This was a relief to Isaac and helped him to change his attitude towards him when they met at the synagogue.

Simon's wife, however, was not best pleased with Simon when Jesus first came on the scene. She thought that he and his brother were spending far too much time with Jesus and not enough time fishing which was their livelihood! She would have a little grumble when she was with the women at the well and they could see her point of view, specially when Simon would sometimes leave Capernaum and travel with Jesus to neighbouring towns and villages where he would preach and teach the people about God. Simon's wife thought that Simon was becoming too involved with Jesus and neglecting the family business. After all, he was a fisherman first and foremost and not someone to accompany an itinerant teacher and preacher wherever he went around the countryside!

But then all this changed. It changed when her mother who lived with them became ill. She suddenly developed a fever and everyone thought she had been out in the heat of the day too long so she stayed indoors but the following day she was much worse and the fever was raging. She could not get up from her bed and Simon's wife tried to keep her cool by bathing her head with cold water but to no avail. Simon had gone to one of the other villages with Jesus to talk to the people there and his wife sent a message for him to come home as her mother's condition worsened. In fact she rapidly became so ill that everyone around her thought she was dying. Many of the local women gathered outside the house to hear news of the old lady. The sun was beginning to set by the time that Simon and Andrew arrived with Jesus. They went into the house

11

and Simon's wife said that they went straight to where her mother lay and Jesus bent down and looked at her and taking her by the hand spoke to her and immediately she opened her eyes, looked at them, smiled and sat up. The fever had gone and she was instantly well again. Everyone was amazed! Simon's wife was speechless for a few moments----how could this be? How could her mother be cured so instantly? She looked at Jesus and in that moment she knew that here was no ordinary itinerant preacher and teacher; here was someone who possessed some extraordinary power; his eyes were full of love and compassion and she knew exactly what her husband saw in him. This was no ordinary man; this man had a power like no other, accompanied by overwhelming love. She saw it in his eyes and she was so overcome with gratitude and love herself that she seemed incapable of doing the normal hospitable tasks one would normally do and offer a friend who had come into the house! However, her mother came to the rescue and insisted on getting up and helping to get the evening meal for everyone. In the meantime the women who had gathered outside the house were told of the miraculous cure and instead of staying outside to wail and mourn the death of Simon's mother-in-law as they thought they would have been doing, they rejoiced and rushed to their homes telling everyone about the miracle they had just witnessed.

News of Simon's mother-in-law's cure spread throughout Capernaum and soon many people who were sick came or were brought to Jesus for healing. Isaac was among those who were amazed when he heard about these healings and he began to wonder, "Who really is this man Jesus?" Never before had he heard about so many people being cured from so many different ailments;

surely a mere carpenter could not do such things? Maybe Jesus was a prophet? Isaac had heard about the prophets of olden times and when he went to the synagogue there would be readings from the scriptures about prophets but Isaac always imagined them to be extraordinary men not like humble carpenters! For the next few days Isaac couldn't get these thoughts out of his mind.

In the meantime, Simon's wife told the women at the well all about Jesus; her resentment because her husband was spending too much time away from fishing had gone; in fact, she, herself wanted to spend more time with Jesus. This pleased Simon as it had grieved him that she had not been as welcoming towards Jesus as he had been but now these thoughts had gone and she, too, felt an overwhelming outpouring of love when she was in the company of Jesus. She even found herself calling Simon by the name which Jesus had given him, Peter, the rock!

Isaac remembered how the healing of Simon's mother-in-law became the sole topic of conversation in his workshop for days or even weeks following the event. Everyone who came in could talk of nothing else. Even some of the Roman soldiers came into the workshop and asked Isaac about the miraculous cure that had taken place in the town. Although Isaac was extremely interested in hearing about these miraculous cures, he was rather cautious about sharing his interest with the Romans who came in as he thought it could lead to some trouble between the locals and the authority.

Not long after that Andrew, Simon Peter's brother came into Isaac's workshop and he was very excited because of another strange and miraculous thing that had happened. Apparently, he and his brother had gone across the lake to Cana where Jesus wanted to talk to the people there. Crowds of people had gathered on the sloping hillside there, as they heard Jesus was coming and his reputation had gone before him and the people were not disappointed. Jesus addressed the crowds and then suggested they go home but the people were not so easily dispersed; they wanted to hear more of Jesus' teaching. Jesus suggested they should eat but even that would not entice the people to go home so Jesus said they ought to eat there. "Well" said Andrew, "that must have been a joke as how could they feed so many people?" Now, Philip had noticed one young boy in the front of the crowd who had some food with him; apparently he wanted to go to the hillside with his friends but his mother was just cooking the fish for their meal. The boy was so disappointed saying to his mother that everyone was going except him! So his mother relented and gave him a picnic meal of two little fish she had just cooked and some bread. This, the child offered to Philip to share. Andrew said that they were trying not to laugh at the meagre amount that was being offered to share among the whole crowd but Jesus took the offering very seriously and told Andrew and the other friends of Jesus to share it out and this was the most remarkable thing, as they broke it up there seemed to be more and more until there was enough for everyone with pieces left over to be gathered up. It was truly remarkable. Isaac listened to Andrew recounting this amazing happening and was mystified by the whole story.

Chapter 3

One day when Isaac was busy in his workshop a centurion came in from the garrison outside the town. He said that he had heard about the little figures that Isaac carved and he asked if he would do a little wood carving of a cat for him to take home for his niece back in Rome as a present for her. Isaac had seen this centurion before; he was the one who had the reputation of showing kindness to the people of Capernaum, even helping them with the building work on their synagogue. Isaac was happy to oblige and said he would do his best to carve a little cat. How long did he have to do this wondered Isaac and the centurion said that he would be going back to his home in three weeks time so Isaac had three weeks to complete the task. The next day Isaac set to work on it, he had a piece of olive wood which would be just right for it and he decided to carve a cat in a sitting position as that would be easier than attempting to make a cat with four legs supporting it! He did a little bit towards this carving each day between doing his usual run of the mill carpentry work. He had almost finished the cat when Isaac noticed a strange feeling in his right hand or, rather, not so much a feeling but a lack of feeling, a slight numbness. He dismissed it and attributed it to the fact that he had been doing such fine work on the little cat this last week and probably the muscles in his hand had been overworked.

The centurion collected the little carving of the cat and was very pleased with it. He paid Isaac well and promised he would come in when he returned to duty to tell Isaac what his little niece thought of the gift.

A week went by and Isaac noticed that the feeling in his fingers of his right hand was not as it should have been. Rachel also noticed that something was not quite right when he dropped a dish one evening after their meal but when challenged about this, Isaac said he had been working overtime in the past week and he was tired but, secretly, Isaac was worried.

The following week Isaac was asked to do a tricky piece of work down on one of the boats, on Simon's boat so each morning Isaac would walk down to the shore carrying the tools he needed for the job. By the end of the week he noticed that the skin on his foot was not looking good, there was an area of skin that looked different from the rest of his foot and when he touched it he realised that there was a lack of feeling in it. Isaac didn't sleep well that night; there was one word which kept going through his mind and that word was leprosy! Could it be that he had leprosy? Surely not! But this area on his foot combined with the lack of feeling in his hand both pointed to that dreaded disease, leprosy. He tossed and turned all night; if it was leprosy it would be the end of his family life, the end of his business. How could Rachel and the family survive? What would they do without him? The consequences were unthinkable.

The next morning he set about his work with a heavy heart and by the end of the day when the children were in bed Rachel tackled him and asked what was worrying him. Isaac was silent for a moment and then, amongst floods of tears, he told Rachel about his suspicions. She put her arms around him and cradled him in her loving arms and her tears mingled with his for they both knew what the outcome would be. They talked well into the night; they thought of the sequence of events they would have to put into practice, the most important of which would be a visit to the local priest who would look at his hand and his foot and confirm the diagnosis and then he would have to leave his home and his family and live as an outcast outside the town. Even as they spoke about these seemingly inevitable happenings, the thought of them filled them both with dread. They talked well into the night until, exhausted, they fell asleep in each other's arms.

By the next day Rachel already had a plan, she would ask Isaac's father to come out of retirement and work in the carpenter's shop which would provide some income for them and as Isaac was a handy man she worked out that he might be able to build a little shelter for himself outside the town and in the meantime he could use the tent they used when they camped going to Jerusalem for Passover. She and the children would provide him with food each day. Rachel was a very resourceful and practical woman and she was also an optimist and said, "You might get cured of leprosy and then you'll be able to return home." Isaac did not share her optimism but he went along with it because he did not want her to give up hope of him coming back home one day.

Events seemed to swing into action in the days that followed; the family had to be told about the likely outcome of Isaac's symptoms and after many tears and suggestions about his diagnosis, Isaac made his way to the local priest who was sympathetic but had no choice but to give him a little bell, a leprosy bell which Isaac had to ring every time he could see people coming near him so warning them that he was a leprosy sufferer.

17

News about Isaac travelled swiftly throughout Capernaum and when Rachel went to the well in the evening of the following day, most of the women kept their distance as was required by Jewish law because she had been in close contact with someone with leprosy. However, most of the women showed they were sympathetic by smiling at Rachel and some even called out to her saying that their thoughts were with her.

Isaac left the synagogue carrying and ringing his little bell and made his way home for the last time and then, with many tears from Sarah and John, Isaac left for the outskirts of the town. He and Rachel had agreed on the area that he would go to and to which she would bring food for him each day and there, staying at a distance, they would be able to talk to one another.

That evening, Rachel did not go to the well at her usual time; she felt that she did not want to see her friends and neighbours at this time. She knew she would have to keep at a safe distance from them for a while and she disliked the feeling that the topic of conversation among them would most likely be Isaac and his leprosy. The very thought of Isaac being labelled as someone with leprosy sent a shiver down her spine but she knew she would have to learn to live with this fact. However, one fact that she had overlooked was the way it would affect the children; she was prepared to be socially distanced herself, but when Sarah and John came in crying and saying that other children, their friends, would not play with them now, this was hard to bear. Rachel had always been used to solving her children's problems but this was something she could not have anticipated and she didn't know what to do except give them big hugs and assure them that the other children would eventually play with them again.

Each day Rachel would take food and water to Isaac to a place outside the town where they would meet but keeping their distance. Isaac had taken the tent which they had used when going to Jerusalem for Passover in happier times. Rachel would put the food down a few metres away from the tent, Isaac would come and get it and, keeping their distance, they would talk. He always wanted to know how the children were but Rachel kept the problem of their playmates from him as she felt he had enough to cope with in his sudden isolation.

Every day Isaac would go down to the shore in the very early morning when there were not many people about to wash in the water of the Sea of Galilee, each time remembering to take his little bell with him so that he could ring it if he saw someone approaching him. This became a daily routine and then he would return to his tent and wait there until it was time for Rachel to bring him some food. Apart from those two daily occurrences, nothing much happened unless someone he knew passed by at a distance and was brave enough to stop and have a brief conversation with him but this did not happen very often. This was Isaac's new life, a life so different from the one he had lived until it was stolen away by this cruel disease. Not only did this disease steal his life away, but it had taken the life style of Rachel and the children, although he didn't really know the extent of the effect it was having on Sarah and John. On reflection, Isaac wondered if he had been a little too harsh in his attitude towards people with leprosy in the past and through fear of the disease, maybe his insistence to the children that they must never go anywhere near anyone ringing the bell which warned them of leprosy was harsh. He was only trying to protect his family but he had given little thought, if any, to what the person with leprosy must have been enduring! In the past and to his shame, he had regarded people with leprosy with contempt; perhaps they had brought it upon themselves; perhaps it was a punishment for past sins they had committed. Now he was in that position himself, it was the time for his own soul searching. "What have I done in the past that would warrant this denial of my everyday life?" Isaac thought of the many things he was now missing; he missed going along to the synagogue to worship and asked himself why there couldn't be some way in which people with leprosy could be allowed to worship together instead of being cast out and largely forgotten by society and by people who shared the same faith! This was the time when he most needed to hear words of scripture read to him and expounded in the synagogue. He would never again be able to make the journey from Capernaum to Jerusalem for Passover festival and he would not be able to proudly take his son, John, into the part of the temple where the men worshipped. How he had looked forward to that, his son, coming of age. He would have been so proud to accompany him up the Temple steps, through the outer court and the court where the women and children worshipped and into the court where all the men gathered and worshipped together. He would miss all that!

Then he would miss Sarah's and John's weddings when they were old enough to be betrothed. Would Rachel be able to oversee all that on her own? His thoughts turned to Rachel, was it fair that she should suffer as the wife of someone with leprosy? Would she be weary of coming every day with his food? Maybe he should divorce her and set her free to marry someone else, although the thought of Rachel in another man's arms sent shivers down his spine. Suppose he did divorce her and she married someone else and then he, Isaac, got cured of leprosy, he had heard of this happening on rare occasions. What then? He would regret having divorced her and his life, even though he would be free from leprosy would be a life unthinkable without Rachel.

The more he thought about Rachel, the more miserable he became. He asked himself why this had happened to him; why did he get leprosy? There were many people he could think of living in Capernaum who had lived much worse lives than he; some never darkened the doors of the synagogue and they hardly ever gave alms to the poor whereas he, Isaac, had always been generous. These thoughts filled Isaac's head and the words, "Why me?" would not go away.

With so much time on his hands and with nothing to do to fill that time, Isaac became more and more depressed. Winter was now upon them and although Rachel had brought him some extra blankets, the tent remained cold and uninviting. Rachel had suggested that she and the children might carry some pieces of wood from the carpenter's workshop to him so that he might attempt to make a little hut for himself but Isaac had no enthusiasm to do anything! Not only did he miss his family but he missed meeting people, talking to people, listening to them. He loved people coming into his workplace and telling him all their troubles, sharing all their joys and hearing all the latest gossip. Now all that had gone; even Sarah and John did not accompany Rachel as often on her visits and when Isaac asked her why this was so, she said they were busy with their friends, a reason which he did not believe. Isaac felt shut away from humanity. Surely this was not the way God intended human beings to live?

Thinking of God, led Isaac's thoughts to Jesus and he remembered the time when Simon's mother-in-law was healed and the very next day many people had come to Simon's house and Jesus had healed them; not just one or two people but many, although Isaac had not heard whether any of those healed were leprous, probably not! Isaac's thoughts turned to Jesus and how he first heard about this new friend of Simon and Andrew, and was quite worried, because he heard that he was a carpenter. Isaac wondered if he had intended setting up a carpenter's business in Capernaum and he remembered how he felt resentment towards Jesus. But all these fears were set aside as he spoke with Simon and Andrew who told him that Jesus had left his carpentry and was now an itinerant preacher and teacher which was a relief to Isaac and helped him to change his attitude towards him and when they met on Sabbath days at the synagogue, Isaac had to admit that he found Jesus to be a charismatic sort of person. Isaac thought that if Jesus could cure someone who was as near to death as Simon's mother-in-law then, maybe, he could cure leprosy. Perhaps he should ask Jesus for healing? For the following days, Isaac thought of nothing else.

Unknown to him Rachel had been thinking along the same lines; she had been going to the well in the evenings and, whereas some women still kept their distance from her, Rachel noticed that one person showed her much kindness and that was Simon's wife. Until now Rachel had not known her very well but as news of Isaac's leprosy spread throughout the town and many of the women either kept their distance or ignored Rachel, it was Simon's wife who went out of her way to speak to her. It was as if she knew what Rachel was going through, the pain of separation and the rejection by some people. Perhaps she could ask her if Jesus could heal leprosy? Rachel wondered if this was a way for her to be able to meet Jesus and ask him that question herself. So she decided to wait for an opportune time to speak to Simon's wife.

Weeks went by and Passover time was approaching. Isaac knew that many people from the town would be making their way to Jerusalem so when Rachel arrived with his food one day he asked her if she knew who was going to Jerusalem. She mentioned a few names of people that Isaac knew, among them, Simon and his brother Andrew. "Is Jesus going?" asked Isaac but Rachel didn't know and she said she would find out.

On her way back to the house, Rachel wondered why Isaac particularly asked if Jesus was going to Jerusalem and it gave her an idea; this would be a good opportunity to approach Simon's wife to find out a little more about Jesus. So that evening, Rachel made a point of lingering around the well in the hope of seeing Simon's wife but that evening she didn't come. Likewise, the following evening, Rachel lingered over drawing water and this time she saw Simon's wife carrying her water jar with another neighbour. Rachel smiled at her and asked her how she was and if her husband would be leaving soon for Passover at Jerusalem and then casually asked if Jesus was going with them. Simon's wife said that Jesus had already left Capernaum because he intended stopping at some of the villages on the way and to talk to the people in Samaria. This was a surprise to Rachel as good Jews had nothing to do with the people of Samaria, in fact they either ignored them or treated them with disdain and here was Jesus actually purposely going to Samaria! What was Jesus thinking of? But Rachel said nothing;

she said nothing but thought a lot. Rachel then asked Simon's wife how her mother was and was told that she was very well, in fact, she was better than she had been for a long time. Rachel commented that her healing had been miraculous whereupon, Simon's wife agreed and said that Jesus had this wonderful gift of being able to do miraculous things which included healing. Rachel felt that this was her opportunity and asked if Jesus had ever healed anyone with leprosy and the answer was that she didn't know but she felt that nothing was too great a challenge for Jesus.

Those words reverberated in Rachel's head all that night, "Nothing was too great a challenge for Jesus" and she decided that she would tell Isaac that the next day when she took his food. She could hardly wait for the time to go and see Isaac the following day; sometimes Sarah would take food to Isaac but on that day Rachel was anxious to go herself. She left a little earlier than usual and left the food together with a small pitcher of water on the flat stone as usual and called out to Isaac, then, keeping her distance, she told him of her conversation with Simon's wife at the well the previous evening, quoting him the words that had been going around in her head ever since. "Nothing was too great a challenge for Jesus". Isaac listened and a slight smile came over his face. Rachel noticed that this was the first time she had seen him smile since he was diagnosed with leprosy. With this smile on his face he admitted to Rachel that he too had been thinking about Jesus and how he had healed all those people outside Simon's house after healing his mother-in-law. He, too, had been wondering about Jesus as a healer; could Jesus, would Jesus heal him and rid him of this terrible disease? Isaac said to himself that he would wait until Jesus came back to Capernaum and at an opportune time he would speak to him even if it was at a distance.

The days that followed were more bearable for Isaac because for the first time since he had become an outcast, there was a glimmer of hope. Every day Isaac prayed that God would put an opportune time for him to meet up with Jesus and every day Isaac prayed that Jesus would heal him and he repeated the words that Rachel had told him, "Nothing was too great a challenge for Jesus". Isaac found himself desperately trying to remember some of the scriptures he had heard read out in the synagogue. How he wished he could go there again and listen more attentively to what was being read. He remembered that there was a story about a prophet healing someone with leprosy but he couldn't remember who it was, but whoever it was, Isaac remembered that the prophet told this person to wash in a river and although this man was reluctant to do this at first, when he did so he was healed. That story, even though he could not really remember the details, together with the prospect of Jesus coming back to Capernaum gave Isaac renewed hope.

That hope was short lived because the next day as he was walking along the path leading from the sea, Isaac saw two of his friends coming along; Isaac rang his bell to warn them to keep their distance but the two friends just turned the other way and retraced their steps. The fact that neither of them would even stand at a distance and greet him was hurtful and then, later in the day as Isaac walked towards the spot where Rachel would come to bring his food there were some children playing nearby; as soon as they saw Isaac, they all fled in the opposite direction. Isaac felt as if he had turned into some kind of monster to be avoided at all costs! Indeed, there was a high price incurred if one had leprosy. If children and former friends felt like this, maybe Jesus would feel like this too! Perhaps it was too much to expect Jesus to come close enough to heal him. Despair hung over him like a big, black cloud.

Chapter 4

One day, in the following week a Centurion walked into Isaac's workshop asking for Isaac. Rachel, who happened to be around at the time, immediately recognised him as the centurion for whom Isaac had made the carving of the cat. Rachel was a little apprehensive (she was not a lover of the Romans!) and so she did not want to tell him that now Isaac had leprosy and had to live as an outcast so she just said that he wasn't around at that time so could she take a message. The centurion said that his niece loved the carving and he wondered if Isaac could carve another animal by the time he went back to Rome next. Rachel said she would ask him.

While this conversation was going on Sarah and John were in the workshop and when the centurion left Sarah asked her mum why she had not told the centurion that her dad would not be able to carve another animal because he didn't live there or work there anymore. Rachel had always tried to keep up hope of a cure for Isaac in front of the children but now she realised that Sarah had given up hope of their father ever coming back home to live and to work. This came as a shock to Rachel who thought she was doing a good job in keeping the children's hopes up even if she, herself, felt that hope was fading. On realizing this, Rachel broke down in floods of tears; it seemed, in that moment that all was lost and it seemed futile to go on hoping in front of the children.

Rachel could not sleep that night as she continually thought of Sarah's words and after tossing and turning on her bed she suddenly realised that she was allowing herself to give up hope too. The words spoken to her by Simon's wife the previous week had given her renewed hope so why should she dismiss them now? Why should they not be so relevant now? She repeated them over in her mind. "Nothing was too great a challenge for Jesus". These were the words she must keep in her head, these were the words which would keep the spark of hope alive in her and that spark she must try to keep alive in her family, even if everyone else had given up hope. She would wait until Jesus returned from Jerusalem and then think how she would approach Jesus about Isaac.

Meanwhile, the centurion happened to mention to his servant that he had been into the town to try to see the carpenter and wood carver who had carved the little cat for his niece to thank him and to ask him if he would do another carving but he was unable to do this because he wasn't in his workshop. The servant who was a local lad from Capernaum said, " Haven't you heard? He's got leprosy and is now an outcast, living outside the town." "That cannot be" said the centurion, "because his wife said she would tell him that I would like another carving and I said that there was no hurry as it would be a long time before I go back to Rome." The servant assured the centurion that what he had heard was true; most people in Capernaum knew this. The centurion was saddened by this news.

Passover was over and the people returned to their home towns and villages after a few days; Jesus returned to Capernaum together with Andrew and Simon Peter. Rachel heard that Jesus was back in town and she decided that she would go along to Simon Peter's house to speak to Jesus but when she got there, there was no sign of him and she was told that he had got up in the early morning to go into the countryside to pray as he often did, so Rachel returned home where she prepared food to take to Isaac on her daily trip to him outside the town. She didn't tell Isaac that she had tried to see Jesus but during their conversation she did tell him that Simon, Andrew and Jesus had now returned from Passover. Isaac expressed his sadness that he was now unable to go to Jerusalem for Passover and Rachel could tell that this was a big part of his life that he was really missing so she changed the conversation by telling him what John had been learning at school but even this did not really cheer Isaac up as his thoughts turned to the synagogue where John attended school and so it reminded him of the numerous times he went to the synagogue to worship and to hear the words of Holy scripture read aloud on the Sabbath. When Rachel left him she had that feeling of hopelessness, not being able to help Isaac to lift that feeling of sadness, it was a sadness which weighed heavily on Isaac's shoulders and she could do nothing to lessen it.

Isaac sat alone in the little shelter he called his own and after eating the food which Rachel had brought him, he thought again about John going to synagogue school and he pictured in his mind how he would listen to the portion of scripture being read out when he, himself went to the synagogue. He thought particularly about that passage where the man gets cured of leprosy by one of God's prophets all those years ago. If Jesus was a prophet then he would be able to heal him but then Isaac remembered that the man in the story was an important man. If only he could remember his name but whoever he was, Isaac was sure he was someone important, whereas he, Isaac, was not important, he was just an ordinary carpenter living in the ordinary town of Capernaum. Why should he think that he deserved healing any more than any of the other outcast people with leprosy he had seen?

That night Isaac dreamt of his former life, life without leprosy, life with his family, life creating things out of wood and seeing the satisfaction on his customers' faces when he completed a task for them. He woke early, the sun was just rising and Isaac got up and began his early morning walk down the path that led to the shore where he would wash. From this path he could look across and see the part of the town which met the sea; it looked sometimes as if it were to tumble into the sea with the larger building of the synagogue silhouetted against the apricot coloured early morning sky. As he reached the seashore he saw someone walking along the shore and Isaac thought it was unusual for someone to be walking there at dawn but then he looked again, surely it was Jesus walking ahead of him in the dawn sunrise. Isaac quickened his step, no-one else was around and as he got nearer he remembered to ring his bell. He desperately wanted to speak to Jesus but would the sound of his bell make Jesus hurry away as everyone else did when they heard that sound? Jesus went on walking. Isaac walked even faster until he was within hearing distance of Jesus and he then called out to him, "Jesus, it is you isn't it?" Jesus stopped and turned and said, "Yes, it is me". Immediately, Isaac seized his moment and blurted out, " Jesus, please heal me of this leprosy so that I can go back and live with my family and carry on being the carpenter I always was. You healed Simon's mother-in-law and all the people who came to their house that time, now, please, will you heal me?" Jesus took a few steps closer to Isaac so Isaac instinctively rang his bell again so warning Jesus that it was leprosy he had; but still Jesus came closer until he was within touching distance. Isaac thought, "This is the closest I have been to any human being since I became an outcast." Then Isaac looked at Jesus' face, it was a face full of compassion and love and then Jesus raised his hand and touched him on his shoulder, he actually touched him. It was the first human touch that Isaac had felt since he had left home all those months ago. Jesus actually touched him, a man with leprosy! Then he said, "Go and show yourself to the priest." On saying that, Jesus turned and continued on his way.

Isaac stood as if frozen to the spot as Jesus walked away but he knew in that instant that he was going to be healed so he quickly shouted after Jesus. "Thank you, Jesus, thank you, thank you!" Jesus waved to him and went on his way.

Isaac forgot about going to wash in the sea, instead he retraced his steps along the path and gathering his belongings from his shelter he began to walk back into the town. The sun was rising in the sky and as Isaac quickly went along the shore he could see the fishermen unloading their boats from the night's catch. Through the streets he hurried, ringing his bell if he saw someone approaching until he came to the synagogue. It was closed as it was still early in the morning; Isaac would wait until someone opened it. As he waited, he looked at his hands and there were no blotches on them or any signs of leprosy. He looked at his feet and his legs and they, too, looked clean and normal. Isaac was so excited that he thought his heart would burst with joy and thankfulness. What seemed like an age but was probably only about half an hour, the man who looked after the synagogue opened the door. Isaac said "Where's the priest, I must see the priest!" The man who opened the door recognised Isaac as the carpenter who had leprosy so he said, "Where's your bell? You know you must ring your bell when you come into the town!" "Here's my bell!" replied Isaac, ringing it right up close to the man's face, "but I don't need it anymore as I've been healed of my leprosy". The doorkeeper looked at Isaac long and hard and thought that he looked alright but said, "Well the priest will know if you've been healed or not so wait there by the door until he comes." Isaac waited and after what seemed like a long time but probably wasn't very long really, the priest arrived and Isaac was invited into the synagogue. There the priest carefully examined Isaac's body and had to admit that he could find no sign of leprosy. The priest confirmed what Isaac had been waiting to hear ever since he had been in this synagogue at the start of his banishment.

"Well," said the priest, "I can find no sign of leprosy anywhere on your body. Did it just go and was it gradual or did it go suddenly?" "No" replied Isaac, "I was healed by Jesus". "Do you mean the preacher from Nazareth?" asked the priest. "Yes" said Isaac. The priest looked a little sceptical, "I've heard that this man has healed people in Capernaum of many ailments but you are the first person I've seen that has been cured of leprosy. All I hope, for your sake, is that the cure lasts!" Isaac was a little taken aback by these words but also a little annoyed that the priest might entertain the idea that this cure might only be a temporary occurrence, inferring that the disease might return. "Well," said Isaac, "do I have your permission to go home?" Reluctantly, the priest agreed as he could find no evidence of leprosy on Isaac.

Pushing his little bell into the bundle of his belongings, Isaac ran through the streets of Capernaum to his house where he banged on the door. Alarmed by such knocking at an early hour, Rachel came rushing to the door. When she saw Isaac she was alarmed, surprised and shocked but before she could utter a word Isaac blurted out, "I'm cured! I'm healed! I am not a outcast any longer! Look at my hands and my feet, the priest has examined me and could find no signs of leprosy. Jesus did it, he healed me!" Rachel was overjoyed and they embraced each other. Sarah and John were awakened by the loud knocking on the door and came running and they, too, joined their parents in their hugs. "No more living apart," said Isaac, "I've come home to be with you all". "Daddy, how did this happen?" asked Sarah. Isaac bent down until his eyes were level with Sarah's and said, "Jesus healed me, he touched me and in that touch came the healing that I longed for, that I prayed for."

Chapter 5

News travelled fast by word of mouth in the town of Capernaum and Isaac's miraculous healing was no exception. First it was the neighbours and Isaac's father who were the first to know. Rachel was so excited that she rushed down the hill to Simon's house to tell them the good news. Simon's wife was delighted but not all that surprised to learn that Jesus had brought about the healing; other people were, at first, a little more sceptical asking themselves if Jesus really had the power to heal leprosy as instantly as that. Meanwhile, there was much rejoicing in Isaac's house and among his immediate neighbours. That night when Sarah and John were in bed, Rachel and Isaac discussed what had happened. Isaac said how he had been thinking of the story of the prophet who had healed an important man of his leprosy which he had heard read from the Holy Scriptures at the synagogue and Isaac said how he had prayed long and hard to God for a cure for himself. He also said that he was convinced that Jesus was not just a carpenter who had become a teacher and preacher; Jesus was, in his eyes, a great prophet and he had decided that, above all else, he must know more about him and listen to his teaching. Isaac said that he now understood why Simon and Andrew spent such a lot of their time with Jesus. Rachel agreed that they would go and listen to Jesus the next time they knew he was preaching near them.

The news of Isaac's healing was very good for his business; people came to him, not just wanting work done but to see for themselves that his leprosy had been cured so Isaac found himself busier than ever, repairing and making pieces of furniture and also carving small figures out of wood. All the feeling of numbness which he had experienced when the disease first took hold had gone and his fingers were as sensitive and nimble as they had ever been.

Among the people who heard about Isaac's miraculous cure was the lad who was the servant to the centurion for whom he had carved the little cat. He told the centurion who said that he would call and see him for himself when he next went into town. Sure enough, the following week the centurion paid Isaac a visit. Rachel had forgotten to tell Isaac that he had been to the workshop asking for another carved figure.

When the centurion came into Isaac's workshop he told Isaac how delighted his niece had been with the cat carving and he would like Isaac to do another carved figure for him to take home when he next went. This would not be for many months so there would be plenty of time. Isaac agreed and then the centurion asked him about his leprosy and Isaac told him the whole story. The centurion was intrigued and asked questions about Jesus but, although Isaac's immediate reaction was to enthuse about Jesus, he was also very aware that the man to whom he was speaking was a Roman soldier and they were all living under Roman rule. The last thing that Isaac wanted was to get Jesus into any kind of trouble so when the centurion asked him where Jesus lived and where he had come from, Isaac was rather vague in his replies even though this centurion did seem different from many of the Roman soldiers from the garrison. The centurion left the workshop promising that he would return at some time for the carving but, as he said, there was no rush to get it done.

Isaac was kept busy in his workshop over the next few weeks, he thought how his miraculous healing was certainly good for business but whenever he had some spare time he would go down the hill to Simon Peter's house as he loved hearing him talk about Jesus. Sometimes, Jesus would be there and Isaac could listen to him and talk with him. He learned a lot from listening to Jesus, although some of his teaching he found rather difficult. When Isaac asked Jesus why he had made a point of visiting Samaria when on his way to Jerusalem. (He knew that most devout Jews went out of their way to avoid going through Samaria.) Jesus replied by asking Isaac if he would help a Samaritan who came to him for assistance. Isaac thought for a moment; what would he really do? His first instinctive response was that he would make an excuse not to help him but, somehow, he knew that this would not be what Jesus would do so Isaac found himself saying that he would try to help. However, deep down in his heart Isaac knew that he would think twice about offering any help. When he walked back up the hill to his own house he thought a lot about the answer he had given Jesus. He had been brought up as a good, devout Jew and traditionally devout Jews did not mix with Samaritans because they were not considered to be "true Jews". This had been so since the time of the division of the kingdom in olden times; at the time of this division, Jerusalem was the capital of the southern kingdom and Samaria was the capital of the northern kingdom. When King Ahab became the king of the northern part he built a temple to a pagan god for his inhabitants to worship in their own kingdom.

Then, when the Assyrians conquered Samaria, they resettled the land with foreigners so the hatred of the Samaritans was also a racist attitude which passed on down the generations. Now, here was Jesus, a Jew, challenging the traditional attitude which the Jews had towards the Samaritans! Isaac thought about this as he walked back home. Jesus had certainly given him something to think about. Was Isaac's attitude towards Samaritans really justified?

It was not only his attitude towards Samaritans which Isaac was now questioning; since his leprosy and his enforced isolation, his attitude towards people with leprosy had most certainly changed. Whereas, previously he had given little thought to the changes they had to make in their lives and the lives of their families if they caught leprosy, now he found himself being much more compassionate towards them. He was also more compassionate towards anyone with a disability. He realised this when visiting the local market place where he had frequently seen a man, unable to walk, lying on his bed mat asking for alms. In the past, Isaac would have dropped a few coins into his begging bowl and walked on but now he wondered about this man. How did he get to the market place? Where did he live and did he have any family? All these thoughts went through Isaac's mind. Then, one Sabbath, he saw him outside the synagogue so Isaac stopped, gave him some money and asked him how he got there. The man told him that he relied on members of his family and friends to carry him there on his bed mat. Each day when they could, they would carry him to a place where there was likely to be a number of people passing by and leave him there until later in the day when they would return to carry him home.

Isaac thought about this on his way home from the synagogue; how awful for this man to be reliant upon friends and family to go anywhere. There was no freedom for this man in his life. What prospects did he have? He would always be totally reliant upon others for everything. At least, when Isaac had his leprosy he still had the freedom to walk about even though he was limited by the fact that he always had to be socially distanced from others. If only this man could meet Jesus, maybe, he too could be healed.

From that day on, Isaac always stopped to talk to this man whenever he saw him, whether it was at the market place or near the synagogue or wherever his friends had taken him. Isaac got to know him quite well and discovered that his name was Josiah. One day when speaking to him, Isaac asked him if he had heard of Jesus, Josiah said that he had heard of Jesus and he had heard that he was a preacher of some kind and that he had healed some people but he didn't know if that was true or not. Isaac assured him that this was true and then Isaac told him about his own miraculous healing, how he had been struck down with leprosy and was compelled to live as an outcast but Jesus had healed him and freed him of his leprosy. Josiah listened intently and began to wonder if this Jesus would heal him and make his legs strong enough to hold him and help him to be able to walk. Isaac assured him that Jesus seemed to be able to cure anyone so he suggested that his friends might like to take him to a place where Jesus might be so that he could meet him. Josiah said that he remembered seeing Jesus go to the synagogue so that might be a good place for his friends to take him.

A few days went by and Isaac was working on a piece of furniture when some young men came in and wanted to speak to him about Jesus. They said they were friends of Josiah and they wanted to know more about Jesus. Isaac suggested that they go and listen to Jesus for themselves and this they agreed to do and sure enough later that week when Jesus was teaching a crowd of local inhabitants, Josiah's friends went along to listen. Now they had been brought up as "good, traditional" Jews, going to the synagogue, listening to the scriptures being read out but when they listened to Jesus, he spoke of God who loved all equally whether you were Jews or Gentiles, rich or poor, whether you were of priestly origin or not; everyone was important and loved by God. The friends listened and their thoughts turned to Josiah

The next Sabbath day Josiah's friends carried him to the synagogue and left him on the steps near the entrance but people said he was in the way there so could his friends move him a little further away from the door. All day Josiah lay there, people passed him on their way into the synagogue and many gave him alms but the one person he wanted to see did not come that day and so a disappointed Josiah greeted his friends when they came to carry him home. The next few days saw him back at the market place and Isaac saw him there. Isaac was disappointed that Josiah had not seen Jesus but he tried to cheer him up by saying that he was sure he would see Jesus some time soon. A few days after that, Isaac was in his workshop when someone came in and said they were going to listen to Jesus who was speaking at a house not far away from Isaac's workshop. Isaac pricked up his ears and asked them exactly where Jesus was. Having established exactly where he was, Isaac rushed out to the market place to look for Josiah. Sure enough Josiah was lying on his mat in the market place. "Where are the friends who carry you here?" asked Isaac. Josiah told him where they lived and Isaac set off to find them; on finding two of them, Isaac quickly explained what he wanted and leaving an urgent message for the other two friends they left for the market place. However, by the time they arrived at the house where Jesus was, crowds of people had already gathered inside and there was no way in which they could carry a man on a bed mat into the house. They tried asking the people to make room for Josiah to be carried in but there were so many people all intent on listening to Jesus that Isaac could see that there would be no way in through the door. Undeterred, Isaac had an idea, "Let's take him up to the roof and let him down to the place where Jesus is speaking" he said to the others. The friends thought this was a good idea so, with some difficulty they managed to carry him up to the roof whist Isaac tore his sheet into strips to form ropes to let him down. Isaac knew all about the structure of these houses and they carefully began to uncover a piece of the roof to make a hole. The people inside the house were surprised to feel small pieces of roof falling on them and some said "Is it an earthquake?" but then they saw what was happening and they made a space for Josiah to be let down onto the floor in front of Jesus. Jesus looked at Josiah and then looked up at the friends who had brought him there and declared that their faith was amazing and then, turning to Josiah he spoke to him and taking his hands, Jesus helped him stand and then take a few steps. Josiah found that not only were his legs strong enough to hold him but he could actually walk! A wave of amazement crept through the crowd; everyone in that house wanted to see Josiah for themselves, to see him walk unaided. His friends were ecstatic, their mission had been accomplished and Isaac was as delighted as they were. From that day many people became Followers of Jesus .

A few weeks later Isaac was in his workshop when in rushed two Roman soldiers. They seemed to be on a mission which made Isaac feel uncomfortable. They asked Isaac if he knew where Jesus was as they had orders from their centurion to find him. Isaac was fearful. Why did they want to find Jesus? Was Jesus in danger? Isaac knew that the Jewish authorities were not very happy with the growing popularity Jesus was attracting but why did these soldiers want Jesus? Then all his fears disappeared because the soldiers told him that the centurion who sent them told them to come to Isaac because he would know where Jesus was. The soldiers went on to say that the centurion's servant was ill and he wanted to ask Jesus to heal him. Immediately Isaac knew that it would have been the centurion for whom he had made the wood carving and he knew that he had shown much interest in Jesus after he had heard of Isaac's healing. Isaac came out of his workshop to take the soldiers to where they might find Jesus. As usual, when they found Jesus he was surrounded by a group of people listening to him. The two soldiers conveyed their message to Jesus and Isaac spoke up for the centurion saying that he was sympathetic towards the people of Capernaum and that he had been very interested to learn more about Jesus after he knew of Isaac's healing. Jesus agreed to go with the soldiers to the centurion's house and Isaac and some of the crowd followed. They had not gone far along the road when someone from the centurion's house came with a message for Jesus from the centurion. The message was to tell Jesus not to come to his house as he felt he was not worthy to welcome so great a teacher and healer to enter his home. Instead, he had faith that if Jesus was just to say the word, then his servant would be healed! Jesus was amazed at the faith of the centurion and indeed, so was Isaac who learned later that the servant was healed at that very hour. Jesus commented, "I have not seen such faith, in the whole of Israel".

Isaac was pleased for the centurion and his servant but he was also pleased because he felt that he had contributed a little towards the servant's healing for if he had not told the centurion about his recovery from leprosy which Jesus had brought about, then he might not have thought of asking for his servant's healing.

Above: Boat on the Sea of Galilee

Below: Boats similar to those used in Jesus' time

Above: The Sea of Galilee at Dawn

Left: Ruins of the synagogue at Capernaum as it is today

Chapter 6

This was to be the Passover like no other thought Isaac as the time for Passover was fast approaching. How Isaac had missed celebrating Passover when he had leprosy! This was another of the parts of life that was denied him: leprosy had stolen that from him. At Passover time Isaac's thoughts were with all his family and all the other families who would be celebrating together in their family groups reminding themselves of the time, years ago when they, as a nation, came out of slavery and could return to the Promised Land. There they could live as free citizens and not be subject to any taskmasters. When Isaac was banished from his family, friends and neighbours because of leprosy, he missed all this. In fact, living alone as an outcast made him more aware of the meaning of Passover; he wondered what his ancestors' lives were like when they were slaves in Egypt. Being slaves to Pharaoh all those years ago must have been degrading for the Israelites, just as being an outcast because of leprosy which forced him to live apart from all those he knew and loved, his family and his friends, all this was degrading for Isaac. Being dependent upon the Egyptian taskmasters for everything, that was degrading for his ancestors all those years ago. Being dependent upon his wife, Rachel, bringing him food and water when he had leprosy, this was degrading as he should have been the breadwinner, the one on whom the family relied. All these thoughts had filled Isaac's head when he lived as an outcast. But now, since he had been healed of his leprosy and his life had been restored to him by Jesus, now it was time to celebrate and Isaac was determined to make this Passover not just a celebration of the Israelite nation's freedom, but a celebration of his own freedom, Isaac's freedom. This year the journey to Jerusalem would be special, it would be a journey of thanksgiving for his own life, a life given back to him by Jesus.

As a family they were looking forward to going up to Jerusalem for Passover; they had not gone as a family every year but this year was going to be special and Sarah and John were excited at the prospect. Isaac was pleased that the children were looking forward to it as much as he had done so as a child. The extended family with whom they would share the Passover meal in Jerusalem would ask John, Isaac's son, to ask the important question at the meal as he would be the youngest there and traditionally, the youngest member present would ask, "Why are we doing this?" and the oldest member would recall the reasons for the traditions they were upholding. The story, their story, would be retold so that they would never forget.

Many families would travel together to Jerusalem, camping on the way and Isaac's family would join with others from Capernaum. Isaac heard that Jesus, accompanied by Simon Peter, Andrew and some of the other followers of Jesus had already left for Jerusalem and they intended staying there a little longer. Isaac could not afford that much time away from his business so he and Rachel arranged to go with a small group to arrive in Jerusalem a day or so before Passover. This was certainly going to be a Passover like no other thought Isaac.

The journey to Jerusalem was uneventful, except that there seemed to be more people than usual making their way that year and many of them travelling along the road talked about Jesus. He had got quite a reputation around Capernaum but Isaac was surprised and delighted to learn that people from much further afield not only knew about him but believed in his teaching.

As they approached Jerusalem, they met people on the road who had been in Jerusalem for a few days and they were extremely excited because Jesus had ridden into the city on a donkey on the previous Sunday. Apparently, people had rushed out to meet him and they waved palm branches and lay palm leaves down on the road for the donkey to walk over. It was just like a parade, a parade fit for a king with the crowds shouting "Hosanna! Blessed is he who comes in the name of the Lord!" Isaac was excited by this; did it mean that something wonderful was about to happen? Would Jesus claim kingship for himself?

When they got into the city Isaac managed to see some of the disciples who confirmed the rumours they had heard about the procession on the previous Sunday. But they also told Isaac that the religious leaders were not happy with the enthusiasm and popularity being shown towards Jesus. This was leading to tension between the religious leaders and the enthusiastic crowds and this was not what the Roman authorities wanted at any cost. This tension was such that it made Isaac and Rachel instil upon Sarah and John that they must always stay close to them while in the city. They visited the Temple, only to hear that Jesus had gone there the previous day and had been very angry with the money changers and the people selling animals for sacrificing in the outer court of the Temple. Isaac said that was a good thing as he always thought the stall holders and the money changers over-charged the people. On going inside the Temple, they found Jesus there surrounded by a group of people. He was teaching them and explaining the scriptures to them. Isaac and his family joined them and sat and listened as he explained what was meant by the Kingdom of God.

The day of Passover arrived and they joined with the extended family for the traditional meal of bitter herbs, lamb and wine. However, the meal was somewhat marred by rumours that the Temple guards were anxious to find an excuse to stop Jesus from teaching in the temple as he was attracting such crowds, larger crowds than the Pharisees or the Scribes could ever attract; Isaac thought it was just jealousy on their part.

The following day would be the last day for Isaac and the family to be in Jerusalem before starting off on their homeward journey. They awoke to hear the news that Jesus had been arrested and was being tried in court that day. Isaac was devastated, surely they could not arrest a man who had done such good deeds! Isaac decided to delay his homeward journey until later as he was anxious to hear the outcome of the trial. As the day wore on, the news did not sound good. Not only were the temple authorities involved but also the Roman Governor and that did not sound good to Isaac. However, Isaac thought that Jesus's special friends, his disciples, would speak up for him. Then they heard the most disturbing news and that was that Pontius Pilate was going to release one prisoner as was the custom at Passover and Pilate gave the choice of prisoner over to the crowd, he could release a notorious prisoner called Barabbas or he could release Jesus. Isaac was in the crowd but his voice was barely heard above the cries of the majority shouting, "Release Barabbas! Release Barabbas!" So Jesus was led away to be crucified outside the city. Isaac could not bear the thought. He walked part of the way through the streets of the city. At one stage Jesus stumbled under the weight of the cross and a Roman soldier who was accompanying them commanded someone walking by in the opposite direction to carry the cross for Jesus. (This was the law at that time, a Roman soldier could order a Jewish person to carry his pack for one mile). Isaac could not bear to follow any longer, he had never actually witnessed a crucifixion and he certainly didn't want to see Jesus whom he knew and admired being crucified so with a heavy heart and a broken spirit he went to meet up with Rachel and the children to begin their journey back home to Capernaum. They would only be able to go a small part of their journey that day before it would be the Sabbath when travelling far was not permitted under Jewish law so they would rest before resuming their journey. This had certainly been a Passover like no other!

Chapter 7

The atmosphere on the trek home was nothing like the atmosphere when they had made the journey a few days before for Passover. It seemed long and Isaac and some of the other families were despondent; they had been proud of Jesus, this prophet who had made his home in Galilee had done so much and he was so popular in Capernaum that they all had high hopes that he would do great things in Jerusalem. Now, all those hopes and all those aspirations, had been dashed and, more than that, they had now lost their dear friend, Jesus. Isaac thought over and over again of all the encounters he had with Jesus and they were all good encounters, the best one, of course, being when he was healed of his leprosy. When Isaac closed his eyes he could imagine once again Jesus touching him on the shoulder and he could hear his voice saying," Go and show yourself to the priest". How could anyone destroy a man who did such good deeds, a man whose very touch could heal and restore a life?

At last they reached Capernaum and the days that followed found Isaac doing the normal things they did except that there seemed to be no joy in doing anything. But then, one of the younger men who had gone to Jerusalem for Passover but who had stayed on a couple of days longer came into the workshop with the most astounding news. He said that the day after the Sabbath Mary Magdalene had seen Jesus and that he was alive and, more than that, the disciples had also seen him as well! Isaac could not believe this young man but he assured Isaac that it was true. Two people from Emmaus had also seen him and had invited him into their home to share a meal! Isaac could hardly believe what his ears were hearing and it was no good going to ask Simon Peter's wife as they were still in Jerusalem. Isaac prayed that these rumours were not just rumours but that, somehow, and he didn't know how, it would be true. An air of despondency in Isaac's household gave way to an air of hope and expectancy. This feeling increased when Simon Peter and Andrew came back to Capernaum and said first hand that they had seen Jesus. Isaac had difficulty in believing them because, logically, how could someone who had been crucified, someone who had died on a cross and then laid in a tomb, how could anyone survive that? How could he be alive? Isaac discussed this with Peter and Andrew and when Isaac suggested to them that maybe they had seen an apparition or a ghost of Jesus in the Upper room they said, "No, he ate and drank the same as the rest of us." It was all very puzzling. Rachel was convinced that all those who said they had seen Jesus since the crucifixion were really seeing an apparition of him. Her thinking was that the disciples and those close to Jesus were so desperately wanting Jesus to be alive that they had convinced themselves that he was alive but really it was just wishful thinking on their part.

But then Simon Peter and Andrew told others in the town another strange story. They had gone out fishing one night as they were wanting something positive to do to occupy themselves because they were feeling lost without Jesus being with them. They toiled all night but caught nothing so they decided to give up, but as they neared the shore they saw someone standing there in the early dawn light; the man called out to them asking if they had caught any fish and when they replied, this man shouted to them, "Cast your net over the right side of the boat" and when they did so they caught so many fish that they decided to drag the net full of fish into the shore and not to attempt to pull it into the boat. As they approached the shore they recognized the man, it was Jesus! Then they noticed that Jesus had a little fire alight on the shore with a few fish cooking on it; he told the disciples to bring some of the fish they had caught to cook with his fish and then they all had breakfast there on the shore. They were all astounded, not just because they had made a wonderful catch of fish, in fact one of the disciples counted the fish and they numbered 153, but also the fact that Jesus already had a fire alight and was cooking fish! When Isaac remarked that this was wonderful, Simon Peter seemed to have read his and Rachel's thoughts as he said to them, "Ghosts don't light fires, cook fish and then eat it in front of you."

That night, Isaac had a very vivid dream. He dreamt that he was outside the town again in the part where he had lived as an outcast, his hands were leprous but there was Jesus standing before him saying to him those words which Isaac would never ever forget, "Go and show yourself to the priest." But then Jesus said to him in the dream, "Now look at your hands, the leprosy has gone" and as Isaac looked at his hands they were clean and healed. Then, in his dream Isaac saw Josiah standing up before Jesus and not only standing but walking. Isaac awoke and somehow he just knew that the rumours were true. As soon as Rachel woke up, Isaac said to her, "I think the rumours about Jesus being alive are true." Until that moment, Isaac had wanted desperately to believe these tales but his logic had been telling him otherwise and so was Rachel. Then he recalled what he had been told about Jesus raising a dead man to life, he thought his name was Lazarus who lived in Bethany with his two sisters. They had been good friends of Jesus and when Lazarus died, Jesus brought him back to life even though he had been in a tomb for a few days. As Isaac reminded Rachel of this, he said, "If Jesus could heal my leprosy in an instant, if he could make a lame man walk and bring a dead man back to life, then, I think the rumours are true and Jesus is alive." Rachel was not entirely convinced but Isaac seemed sure that he could now believe what the disciples and others were saying. The rumours, although illogical and seemingly unbelievable, now became plausible to Isaac.

Peter and the other disciples went back to Jerusalem and Isaac heard that they began teaching and preaching boldly just as Jesus had done and they were attracting crowds of eager listeners. Someone who had been in Jerusalem came into Isaac's workshop and told him that Peter had even healed a crippled man! Isaac was amazed and wanted to know more. He was told that it happened at one of the entrances to the Temple, the one called "The Beautiful Gate" where this crippled man was asking for alms. Peter and John were walking into the Temple when this man begged for alms from them. Peter told the man that they didn't have alms to give him but instead, Peter told the man to get up and walk in the name of Jesus Christ and the crippled man did just that! Isaac was immediately reminded of the words Jesus spoke to him when he said, "Go and show yourself to the priest." These were just words but what powerful words! Isaac thought that the priests and all the Sanhedrin would have been pleased that the crippled man was healed but this was not so and Peter and John ended up in prison because of their teaching. Isaac could not understand this and he asked himself the same question he had asked when Jesus was crucified, "How can the authorities condemn someone who does such good deeds and appears to possess such powers?" It really was very puzzling and as weeks turned into months and more people became Followers of the Way, the more the authorities stirred up trouble for them. Isaac was told that he should keep quiet about his belief in Jesus or it might affect his business, in fact, it had already affected his business a little because he knew of some customers who used to enter his shop frequently, did not visit now. But Isaac continued to have faith in the group of Followers and he also remained a worshipper at the local synagogue even though some long standing worshippers tended to ignore him. He scratched the shape of a fish onto a pebble as this was the secret sign for the Followers of Jesus and put it on a shelf in his workshop alongside the bell he had been forced to carry when he had leprosy. Any Follower coming into his workshop would know that he, Isaac, was a Follower when they saw the sign on the stone but to anyone not a Follower, they would just see it as a fish scratched on a stone.

A few months passed and one day a man came into Isaac's workshop whom he did not know. He could see that he was not from the vicinity around Capernaum. Isaac asked if he could help him and the man, looking around the workshop spotted the fish etched on the pebble so he said to Isaac, "I see you are a Follower of the Way; are you the carpenter I've heard about who was cured of leprosy by Jesus?" Isaac nodded. Who was this man and what did he want? He went on to explain that he had heard about Isaac and he wanted to hear more about Jesus. "But," said Isaac, "you are not from these parts are you?" The stranger introduced himself by saying that his name was Simon and he was Jewish and came from Cyrene. He said how he had gone up to Jerusalem for the Passover, staying at one of the small villages outside the city with his wife and two sons. He intended staying a few days longer to do business in the city but as he was coming into the city the day after Passover, he had met a crowd of people with soldiers who were leading a man out to be crucified. Well, he had no intention of witnessing such an event but as he stood aside to let them pass by, the man carrying the cross stumbled and fell and a soldier turned to Simon and said, "Hey, you, carry that cross for him!" Roman rules were that a soldier could command a Jew to carry a load for that soldier for one mile and as it was a rule, you didn't argue with that, so Simon carried the cross until they reached Golgotha which was outside the city walls. There he was relieved of his duty but the person for whom he carried it looked at Simon and murmured his thanks. Simon was amazed that anyone who was about to die in this inhumane, cruel manner could even think to turn and say "thank you" to anyone in those circumstances so he thought this unusual. Simon asked someone in the crowd who this person was and what had he done to deserve crucifixion. The person he asked told him that he was Jesus and everyone around had high hopes of him after all the good deeds he had done; in fact many had high hopes that he was the long awaited Messiah, the one for whom they had waited. Simon listened to all this and thought about it for the remainder of the day. That night and the following nights he could not get that man's face out of his mind; he could see him in his mind, a face full of pain and anguish and at the same time, a face full of compassion.

Simon continued, he said that a couple of days passed and he completed his business in Jerusalem and was preparing to return to Cyrene with his wife and two sons, Alexander and Rufus when he heard the most astonishing news. This news was being whispered around among the Followers of Jesus and the news was that Jesus was alive! Now, Simon thought that someone was spreading rumours in the city for no-one could survive a crucifixion because the authorities left the person hanging there until they died; more than that Simon knew that they had placed Jesus' body in a tomb. How could anyone survive that? However, all the way back to Cyrene, Simon pondered about this because those telling these tales were reputable people. He thought about this so much that he felt he wanted to hear more, so after a couple of months he decided to make the return journey to Jerusalem. He could justify his visit as he could attend to some business while he was there. This time he travelled alone while his wife stayed at home in Cyrene with the boys.

Simon continued with his story, telling Isaac that he had gleaned a lot of information about Jesus in Jerusalem and all he heard increased his curiosity and his thirst for more knowledge about him and his teaching. He had met some of the Followers but he was told that if he came to Capernaum he would find Simon Peter's family there and he might be able to meet some of those who had been healed by Jesus, Isaac being among them.

On hearing all this, Isaac invited him to stay with him and the following morning he would take him to meet Simon Peter's wife and his brother, Andrew. This Isaac did and after hearing more about Jesus and his teaching from the disciples, Simon, the Cyrenian became a Follower of the Way and he left saying that he would relate all he had learned about Jesus to his wife and boys with the hope that Alexander and Rufus would be Followers too. They agreed that they would meet up again in the future, maybe, for a Passover so they parted with the words "Next year in Jerusalem".

Epilogue

Isaac looked intently at his two most precious possessions, the bell and the pebble, both of these symbolised a huge part of his life. He wondered if his grandson, Joseph would be happy to become a Follower of the Way and believe in the teachings of Jesus when he grew up. Since those early days when Isaac had first met Jesus, so many people had joined them and so many people had suffered because they had become believers, some had even been stoned to death because of their beliefs! However, in spite of this persecution, there were now groups of believers in other countries as well as Judea, Galilee and even Samaria and some said that there were groups as far away as Rome and beyond and not all these new followers were Jews. Many of the new Followers of the Way were Gentiles. Maybe, if Jesus was the promised Messiah, could he have been the Messiah for Gentiles as well as Jews? Isaac had always been brought up to think that they, the Jews, were a chosen group of people but, perhaps Jesus came to be a Messiah for Jews and Gentiles?

Isaac thought back to the time when he had gone to Jerusalem for Passover, alas, he did not go to the city to celebrate now because it had become too dangerous for the Followers of Jesus to be there. The Pharisees were determined to eradicate the teachings of Jesus but the more they tried to stamp it out, the more the groups of Followers seemed to grow. The disciples themselves had scattered away from Jerusalem and had gone to numerous places, so taking the message to countries far and wide.

Isaac sighed. He still could not see how Jesus did not receive the recognition he deserved. Was it jealousy? Maybe it was because those in high places did not expect the Messiah to come as a humble carpenter but they expected someone more like them, someone with authority and a high social standing. This was exactly what Isaac saw as the greatness of Jesus, it was his humility, even though he possessed such divine power.

Looking at his bell, Isaac thought about the time when he had leprosy; in retrospect he had learned so much from it. Of course it was an awful time in his life, the rejection by many, the isolation, specially the isolation of being cut off from his family, those he loved and the companionship of friends. There were other things he missed, such as not being able to go to the synagogue and not being able to carry out the rituals associated with his religion but what he learned was that he didn't need to go to the synagogue to pray to God and he didn't need to carry out all the rituals demanded by the Pharisees. Of course, he missed hearing the scriptures being read out from the scrolls in the synagogue but he learned that his relationship with God became more real when he was forced to spend hours on his own.

Isaac did not do much carpentry these days, he leaves that to his son; he considers himself to be of that older generation which could take life a little slower. Peter does not do much fishing, either, but whereas Isaac considered himself to be rather old to work, Peter was still travelling around preaching and teaching people about Jesus. Nothing, not even persecution would stop him and Isaac heard that he had been hauled up before the authorities and was thrown into prison but had a miraculous escape. Peter, through his faith appeared to have gained some of the attributes of Jesus even to the point of raising a woman to life again in her home town of Joppa. News of that event travelled quickly throughout the region.

It was all this that the sign of the fish etched on the pebble brought to Isaac's mind and as for the bell? Not only did it remind him of that awful yet special time in his life, it also was a constant reminder not to be too harsh in judging others; leprosy is not a respecter of persons and the owner of such a bell needs compassion, help and sympathy.

That is why these two objects were so important to Isaac and he hopes the stories behind them will help his grandson to follow in his footsteps and become a Follower of the Way

About the Author

Margaret Williams was born, brought up and educated in Swansea, South Wales. Qualifying as a teacher, she began her teaching career also in Swansea but moved to Swindon when she married where she taught in a number of schools and became headteacher of Lainesmead Infant school. She was the first headteacher of a newly built church school, namely, Oliver Tomkins Church Aided school where she remained until she retired. She served on the Bristol Diocesan Board of Education for many years and was Chairman of the House of Laity for the Bristol Diocese from1994 – 2000.

Margaret was one of the first women to be licensed as a Lay Minister in the Church of England, a licence which she still holds today and exercises at Christ Church, Swindon. The story of her initial years as a Female Lay Reader has been told in her first book, "Bridging the Gap" published in 2007.

In 2015 Margaret was awarded an MBE in the New Year's honours list for services to the church and community.